WILLIAM M. GAINES'S

THE NON-VIOLENT
MAD®

ALBERT B. FELDSTEIN, Editor

WARNER BOOKS

A Warner Communications Company

THERE IS ALWAYS A TENDENCY
TO GENERALIZE
ABOUT MEMBERS OF SOCIAL AND
ETHNIC GROUPS.

THIS NEXT ARTICLE
IS CALCULATED TO SHOW
THE IDIOCY OF

STEREOTYPE-
CASTING

...BY THE
NUMBERS

ARTIST: BOB CLARKE

ONE CHINESE

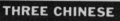

is a
LAUNDRY

TWO CHINESE

is a
RESTAURANT

THREE CHINESE

is an
IMMIGRATION QUOTA

FOUR CHINESE

is a
POPULATION EXPLOSION

ONE FRENCHMAN

is a CHEF

TWO FRENCHMEN

is a POLITICAL PARTY

THREE FRENCHMEN

is a MARRIAGE

FOUR FRENCHMEN

is a FILM FESTIVAL

ONE SOUTH AMERICAN

is a
BULLFIGHT

TWO SOUTH AMERICANS

is a
NEW DANCE CRAZE

THREE SOUTH AMERICANS

YANQUI GO HOME!

is an
ANTI-U.S. MOB

FOUR SOUTH AMERICANS

WE LOVE ^YANQUI GHOE!

is a
FOREIGN AID PROGRAM

ONE TEENAGER

**is a
TELEPHONE TIE-UP**

TWO TEENAGERS

**is a
DRAG RACE**

THREE TEENAGERS

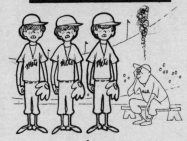

**is a
N.Y. METS OUTFIELD**

FOUR TEENAGERS

**is a
BEACH MOVIE**

ONE ITALIAN

**is a
PIZZA PARLOR**

TWO ITALIANS

**is a
BARBER SHOP**

THREE ITALIANS

**is a
SENATE INVESTIGATION**

FOUR ITALIANS

**is an
OPERA**

ONE ARAB

**is a
BRITISH PROTECTORATE**

TWO ARABS

**is a
BORDER WAR**

THREE ARABS

**is a
U.N. CRISIS**

FOUR ARABS

We Love you Omar

**is an
OMAR SHARIF FAN CLUB**

ONE TEXAN

is a
MARLBORO COMMERCIAL

TWO TEXANS

is an
OIL MONOPOLY

THREE TEXANS

is a
JOHN WAYNE MOVIE

FOUR TEXANS

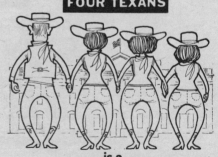

is a
"GREAT SOCIETY"

ONE NEGRO

is
TOKEN INTEGRATION

TWO NEGROES

is a
CHAMPIONSHIP BOUT

THREE NEGROES

is an
EMERGING AFRICAN NATION

FOUR NEGROES

is
SAMMY DAVIS, JR.

ONE BEATNIK

is a POETRY READING

TWO BEATNIKS

is a TRIAL MARRIAGE

THREE BEATNIKS

is a PROTEST GROUP

FOUR BEATNIKS

is an UNEMPLOYMENT LINE

ONE ENGLISHMEN

**is a
PARLIAMENT MAJORITY**

TWO ENGLISHMEN

**is a
BORE**

THREE ENGLISHMEN

**is an
EXPEDITION**

FOUR ENGLISHMEN

**is a
NEW SINGING GROUP**

ONE IRISHMAN

is a
POLICE FORCE

TWO IRISHMEN

is a
FIGHT

THREE IRISHMEN

is a
WAKE

FOUR IRISHMEN

is a
PARADE

ONE JEW

**is a
SMALL BUSINESS**

TWO JEWS

**is a
SMALL BUSINESS & SON**

THREE JEWS

**is a
COMEDY-WRITING TEAM**

FOUR JEWS

**is a
CATSKILLS RESORT**

TWO MAD READERS

**is a
DROP-OUT**

**is a
LUNATIC FRINGE**

THREE MAD READERS

**is a
DISASTER AREA**

FOUR MAD READERS

**is our
TOTAL CIRCULATION**

Hey, Gang! Here we go with this "MAD Newsletter" treatment of one of the most ridiculous college farces in recent years. And we don't mean "Phone-Booth-Stuffing" or "Gold-fish-Swallowing"! We mean "Movie-Making"...mainly the one they made about a group of graduates from a posh all-girl's school. First--so you can follow who's who--which is more than most people could do for the first half hour of the picture--we'd like to present the elite members of

ARTIST: MORT DRUCKER
WRITER: ARNIE KOGEN

"THE BUNCH"

FLAKEY . . . Mona Lisa of the smoking room! She was expelled from school for kissing on her first date . . . mainly for kissing Miss Tittle, the Dean of Girls!

DUDDY . . . They told her thin girls are more sensual, and she believed them—until she saw her first stag movie in the dorm, starring Phyllis Diller doing a strip tease!

PRISSY . . . She was a frail flower among the weeds . . . a tender and sensitive child! Her face would break out in a terrible blotchy red rash during Final Exam week.

PILLY . . . She caused quite a commotion at Vassar when she kept snapping wet towels at everyone in the shower room—mainly because it was the Princeton shower room!

KAYO . . . Her marriage was quickly destroyed by temper tantrums and infidelity . . . and her career was quickly destroyed by sloppy direction and a terrible script.

PUKEY . . . Money, money, money! She was wealthy and eccentric! For example, she actually hired a tutor to help her cram . . . for the "TV National Health Test"!

LIPPY . . . She lied, cheated, screamed—even opened a mouth and yelled a lot—anything to get what she wanted! But she still couldn't get out of her contract to play this role!

HELLUVA . . . She completely destroyed her face . . . which wasn't very beautiful to begin with . . . when she used it to block a punt during a Smith-Vassar Football game!

BIG OPENING SCENE! The girls of "The Bunch" were graduating!

And as we, the Class of '33, go out into these Depression Years, it is up to us to help the poor and downtrodden who are less fortunate—less wealthy than we! Like the Vanderbilts, the Astors and the Rockefellers . . . !

That's Helluva! The most brilliant girl in our Vassar Class of '33!

If she's so brilliant, why is she reading her speech from "Idiot Cards"?

Well, she's certainly the most serious! Why, listen to the courses she took: "Advanced Croquet", "Contemporary Sterling Silver", "Intermediate Snobbery" and "How To Talk To A Maid"! The rest of us took silly, meaningless courses!

Did you say the "Vassar" Class of '33! Oh, excuse me! I'm in the wrong place! The way these girls look, I thought I was at the Harvard Graduation Exercises!

After Graduation, everybody attended THE CLASS DAY DINNER, where each of the members of "The Bunch" announced their plans for the <u>future</u>...

KAYO'S WEDDING! It was such a nostalgic affair! She said, "I do!" and he said "I do!" It was nostalgic because that was the last time the two of them ever agreed on anything!

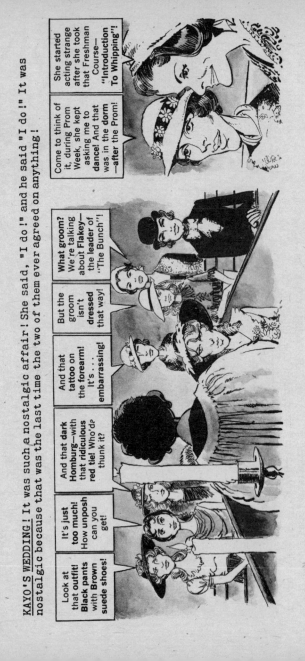

Yep, it looked like *Flakey* was *pretty upset* at not being invited on *Kayo's* honeymoon! Because, for spite, she decided to go off on *one of her own*...

There goes *Flakey*—Off on an ocean liner! How *wild*! How *avant garde*! How perfectly *posh*! That girl will do anything to show off!

What's the big deal? *Lots of College girls* take ocean cruises to Europe!

That's just it! She's hired this ocean liner to sail to *The Bronx!* Next week, she's cruising to Europe!

And they say Vassar girls are snobbish and selfish! Look how democratic *Pukey* is! She's tossing coins into the water and letting the natives dive for them!

But that's the *Hudson River!* The only natives around here are New Yorkers!

They'll dive! Have you forgotten? We're in the middle of a *Depression!*

Next comes the big SEDUCTION SCENE, in which we see the behavior of the kind of girl that comes out of an exclusive Finishing School as compared to, say, a cheap little High School "Drop-Out".

Lippy, the "Gossip" of "The Bunch", had nice things to say about everybody! To play her part, the Producers looked for someone with the biggest mouth around. But Cassius Clay and David Susskind both refused to act in drag...so....

Did you hear the latest? **Pukey** broke out in pimples! Listen, I've seen her complexion! It's an improvement!

Hot news from Europe! **Flakey's** now gallivanting around in **Spain!** Oh, didn't you hear? She was banned in **Paris!**

Prissy had another miscarriage! Oh, well—that's the way the cookie crumbles!

Harold and **Kayo** had a tremendous fight! Lots of hair-pulling, scratching, screaming, and hysterical crying! And poor **Kayo** got pretty upset, **TOO!**

Helluva started some row in **Rome!** One day, she slapped eight Italian men! Why? Because not one of them would pinch her!

What's wrong with you, today, **Lippy?**

I dunno, Pilly! I guess you caught me in one of my good moods! I'm pretty catty on these phone calls **usually!**

Next, Kayo and Harold threw a BIG PARTY! It was a typical Vassar soiree. The discussions involved Roosevelt, Abstract Art, Machiavelli, Fallopian Tubes and George Bernard Shaw. These were discussed by the servants! The Vassar graduates were too busy <u>gossiping</u>!

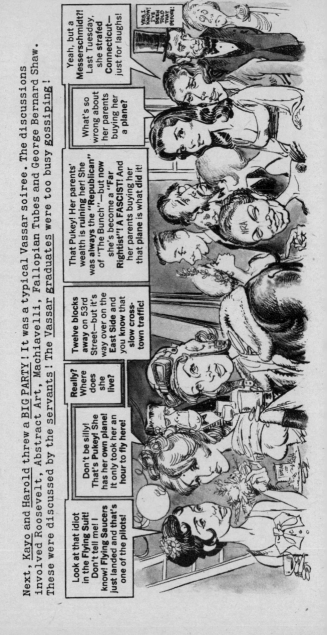

HAROLD, dissatisfied with KAYO'S $9 a week job at Macy's, decided to have an affair with MURINE, who made $11 a week at Gimbels!

Suddenly, everyone started to leave! And with dialogue like that, who can blame them!?!

Harold! You and Murine! Who'da thunk it?

Hey, that's Pukey's line! Besides, in a dramatic situation like this, you ought to be able to come up with something clever!

You're right! After all, I was Valedictorian! Hey—I've got it! How about "Oh, you men! You're all alike!"

Wait! The party's not over! Aren't you going to wait around for the scene where my husband refuses to read his play and burns the script in the incinerator instead?

We heard he was going to burn a script! That's why we waited around THIS long!

But it turns out he's going to burn the WRONG script!

Instead of his PLAY we thought he was going to throw THIS SCRIPT down the incinerator!

Next, LIPPY dropped her Editor and took up with a Norwegian Ski Instructor!

Frigid Ice Maiden! Why don't you kiss me?

I make it a rule—never to kiss a Scandinavian on the first date!

But this is our FIFTH date!

Shows you what kind of an education you get at Vassar! You study Mediaeval Ceramics and Nietzche—but Arithmetic, they never teach you!

And, we found that PILLY had taken up with the Editor that LIPPY dropped for the Ski Instructor!

Pilly, I'm suffering from an anxiety neurosis, a compulsive neurosis, temper tantrums and schizophrenia! I'm morbid and melancholy and what's more I black out a lot!

That's all right, darling! A woman should share the bad times as well as the good!

But you don't understand! These ARE my good times!

POOR KAYO! Her life was filled with danger! Mainly, she got hit on the head a lot...

Next, FLAKEY returned from Europe with a big surprise!

An untimely event now saddened "The Bunch"! They got to see the rushes of the first month's shooting! But still they went on—with the big "Funeral Preparation" scene:

A MAD

Look At Shut-Ins

ARTIST & WRITER: AL JAFFEE

ARTS and CRAFTS

THE
LIGHTER
SIDE OF
TRA

This is the place!

You said it! What a perfect spot to set up our camping gear!

Are you guys nuts or somethin'? Take a look around! Drinking water is two miles back! The nearest swimming is five miles west! And there's no fire wood! Where are all the vital facilities we need?

ELING

WRITER & ARTIST: DAVID BERG

I don't know about the vital facilities **YOU** need, Herman! But the vital facilities **WE** need are all within a **few yards!**

Sure . . . it's way in the **back!**

Oh! Er—thank you, but I'd rather not go!

You mean you're just going to sit there and **suffer?** Why?

I—I don't think I could **stand** having everybody **know** where I'm **going!**

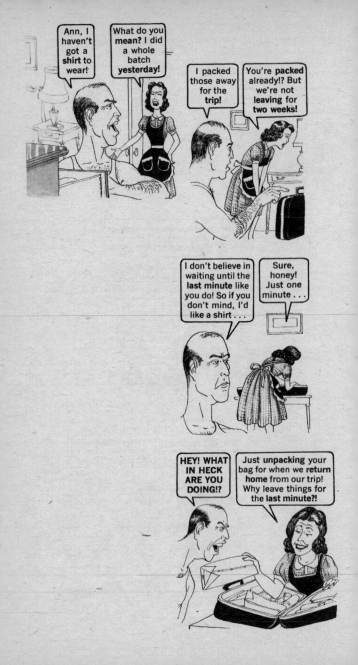

I know I sound like a typical tourist, but—Man! What a view!

Let's see . . . I stopped the milk delivery and the newspapers . . .

Absolutely breathtaking! Le'me get a shot of you in front of this spot . . .

Mrs. Combs said she'd come in and feed the tropical fish every day. I hope she doesn't overfeed them. And I'm worried about the plants I left with Harriet . . .

Now how about taking a shot of me!

Blossom promised she'd come in every night and turn a light on in the house so burglars would think we're home, but Blossom is so forgetful.

Isn't it great to get completely away from all the mundane everyday aggravations of home once in a while!?

HOW SHOULD I KNOW!?

This bus is made up of mostly **new campers!** It's probably **the first** time they've been away from their **families.** We've got a couple of **criers,** and a few on the **verge** of tears. So do something to **cheer 'em up!**

Gotcha, chief . . .

CAMP SHIP-EM-OFF

Hey, Campers! I'm your **Uncle Milty!** Let's **laugh** it up! Let's **sing** it up for good ol' **Camp Ship-em-off!** There's nothing like a good ol' **song-fest** to get into the spirit of **Summer Fun!** Right? Now, what shall we sing?

BE IT EVER SO HUMBLE THERE'S NO PLACE LIKE HOME

Dave Berg

IN THE HOSPITAL

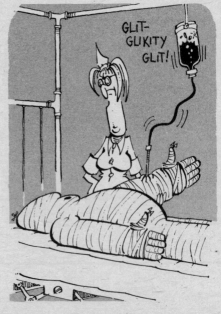

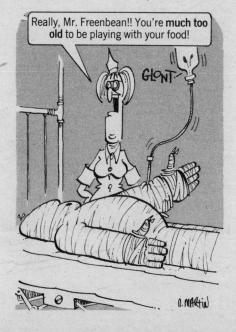

Everybody's going wild over that new TV show featuring "The Caped Crusader" and his teenage side-kick. But has anyone ever wondered what it would really be like as the side-kick of a "Caped Crusader"? Would a typical red-blooded teenage boy really be happy dressing in some far-out costume and spending all of his free time chasing crooks?

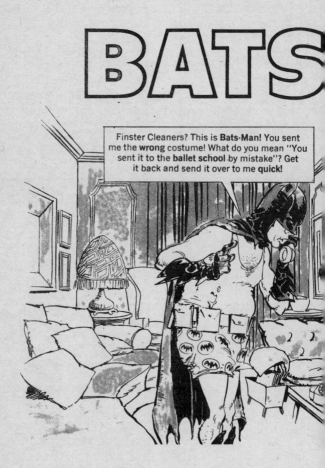

BATS

Finster Cleaners? This is **Bats-Man!** You sent me the **wrong** costume! What do you mean "You sent it to the **ballet school** by mistake"? Get it back and send it over to me **quick!**

ARTIST: MORT DRUCKER

Or would he much prefer dressing in chinos and go-go boots and spending all of his free time chasing chicks? We at MAD think the latter! In fact, we're ready to prove it! Let's take a MAD look at "Boy Wonderful" as he is slowly being driven

WRITER: LOU SILVERSTONE

What's **wrong** with you kids today? Your date will have to wait until evil and injustice have been **erased** from Gotham City! And **after** that, we've got problems in Asia! If you **really** feel the need for feminine companionship, there's always Aunt Hattie!

The Bats-Mobil is all set to go B.M.

Man, that Bat **bugs** me! I ask for one lousy night off and he gives me the whole darn Pollyanna schtick! Okay, baby, you **asked** for it! There's only **one** cat sharp enough to knock you off, Bats-Man, and that's **me**!

This **bomb** attached to the ignition will fix **his** wagon!

TIC TOC TIC TOC

Leapin' Lizards! It's Sparrow Versus Bats-Man!

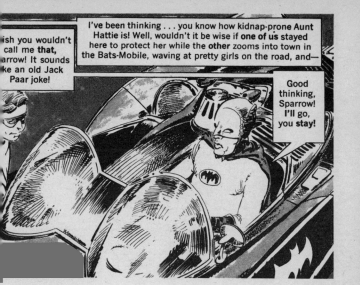

ish you wouldn't call me **that**, arrow! It sounds ke an old Jack Paar joke!

I've been thinking . . . you know how kidnap-prone Aunt Hattie is! Well, wouldn't it be wise if **one of us** stayed here to protect her while the **other** zooms into town in the Bats-Mobile, waving at pretty girls on the road, and—

Good thinking, Sparrow! **I'll** go, you **stay**!

That's better. At least now I look like a **normal** teenager! And in a **few** minutes . . .

Holy Mushroom Cloud! Can That Be The End Of Bats-Man?!

Holy Socks!
What
Bird-Brained
Scheme
Is Sparrow
Hatching Now?

Suffering Sunbeam! Is This The End For Bats-Man, Or Just Another Close Shave?

Well, I tried all the conventional TV weapons and nothing worked. There's only one way left to destroy Bats-Man—expose him!

Holy Perversion, Sparrow! That Would Be Indecent!

Don't you think we ought to close the cave and put the roadblock back up, Bats-Man

Wait a second! I'd know that voice **anywhere**! I **know** who you really are, El Capon—you're **Aunt Hattie**!

Close, Bats-Man, but **not** close enough! You seem surprised . . .

Of course I am! I thought tonight's guest villain was supposed to be Laurence Olivier! But how were you able to make that phone call to the Commissioner? I was with you **all the time**! And how were you able to change into that costume so fast?

A lesson I learned from **you** in one of your many boring speeches! Remember the one about **logic and TV writers**? You were **right**! They have **none**! That's how come we can do things like starting down our Bat-Slide wearing **street clothes** and ending up in the Bats-Cave in **full costume**! But all that doesn't matter now. In a short time you'll be all washed up! **Finished**!

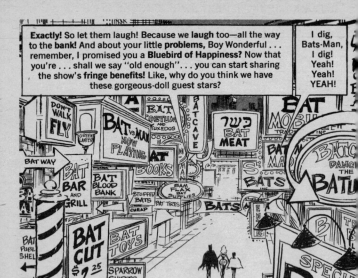

LATER ON IN THE HOSPITAL

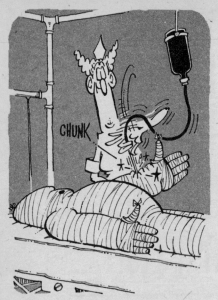

Hey, gang! It's time once again for MAD'S new game. Here's how it works: Take any familiar phrase or colloquial expression, give it an eerie setting so you come up with a new-type monster, and you're playing it. Mainly, you're

HORRIFYING CLICHÉS

ARTIST: PAUL COKER, JR.

WRITERS: PHIL HAHN & JACK HANRAHAN

Laughing At A GROSS EXAGGERATION

Shrinking From A LOATHESOME TASK

Hatching A SCHEME

Laboring Under An ILLUSION

Recalling An OLD INCIDENT

Preserving A FAMILY TRADITION

Lodging A COMPLAINT

Stretching A POINT

Troubled By A NAGGING DOUBT

Losing One's Self In One's WORK

THE TROUBLE WITH ROAD SIGNS IS:
THEY NEVER TELL THE WHOLE STORY.
YOU'LL SEE WHAT WE MEAN AS MAD PRESENTS

ROAD SIGNS

WE'D REALLY LIKE TO SEE

ARTIST: BOB CLARKE   WRITERS: PHIL HAHN & JACK HANRAHAN

DANGER
CONSTRUCTION
WORKERS GOOFING OFF
AHEAD

DETOUR
PREPARE TO GET HOPELESSLY LOST

DOUBLE PARKING PROHIBITED

EXCEPT TO DOCTORS' WIVES
AND SURLY TRUCK DRIVERS

DOCTOR ON CALL

MD·310

PROCEED WITH CAUTION

PAVEMENT CRACKED AND BUCKLING
DUE TO FAULTY CONSTRUCTION AND
INFERIOR MATERIALS USED BY
CONTRACTOR WHO PAID OFF

ENTERING
METROPOLITAN
AREA

**BUMPER-TO-BUMPER TRAFFIC
FROM HERE ON IN**

CITY HALL
PARKING
RESTRICTED

**...MAINLY TO POLITICAL HACKS,
FRIENDS AND RELATIVES OF THE MAYOR
AND THE BOYS IN THE BACK ROOM**

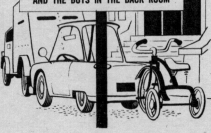

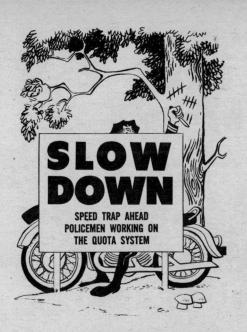

You really can't depend on it, but every once in a while Television comes up with something exciting—like f'rinstance the widely-acclaimed "National Driver's Test." However, this resulted in something you really *can* depend on—mainly that Television always takes anything that is widely-acclaimed and beats the idea to death! Which is why the "National Driver's Test" was followed by the "National Citizenship Test," the "National Health Test," the "National Honesty Test" and the "National Income Tax Test." Which is why we feel that it won't be long before we'll turn on our sets and find these

FUTURE NATIONAL TELEVISION TESTS

WRITER: DICK DE BARTOLO

THE NATIONAL
TEENAGER'S PARENTS TEST

1. At what age should you tell your child about "the birds and the bees"?
   - (a) 12 years old
   - (b) 14 years old
   - (c) 16 years old

   ANSWER: *(a) You should tell your child about "the birds and the bees" when he is about 12 years old. However, you should tell your child about "sex" when he's a lot younger, or he's bound to find out for himself.*

2. At what time should you expect a teenage boy to come home if he has school the next day?
   - (a) 9:00 P.M.
   - (b) 10:00 P.M.
   - (c) 11:00 P.M.

   ANSWER: *(b) You should expect him home at 10:00 P.M. However, you should not be surprised if he shows up at 1 or 2:00 P.M.*

3. A 14-year-old boy is old enough to be forced to take a job.
   (a) True
   (b) False

   ANSWER: (b) *False. It is not fair to expect a boy of 14 to get a job. This is an important time in a boy's life, when he should be outdoors, running and swimming and playing. Of course, it is perfectly normal for you to insist that he do little things around the house, like mowing the lawn, painting the garage, taking out the garbage, simonizing the car, sanding and varnishing the floors, remodeling the basement, shopping, cooking, cleaning, sewing, baby-sitting, etc., etc.*

4. Giving a child blocks to play with will help him face life as an adult.
   (a) True
   (b) False

   ANSWER: (a) *True. Especially if you give blocks around Fifth Avenue and Fiftieth Street.*

5. Petting should be discouraged among teenagers.
   (a) True
   (b) False

   ANSWER: (a) *False. As a matter of fact, teenagers should even be encouraged to play with their dogs. Not only petting, but fetching, rolling over, sitting up, etc. can be stimulating and helpful in developing*

(Cont.)

THE NATIONAL TEENAGER TEST

1. A teenage boy promises to pick up a girl at 8:00 P.M.
He should actually arrive at her house at:
   (a) 8:00 P.M.
   (b) 8:30 P.M.
   (c) 9:00 P.M.

ANSWER: (a) *is correct. If he says 8:00 P.M., he
should arrive at 8:00 P.M. He should
arrive, however, with several good
books, a few crossword puzzles and some
magazines to help pass the time while
waiting for her.*

2. You are a teenage girl, and Friday night is the "big
dance". No one has asked you. As a matter of fact,
every time a boy comes up to you, he suddenly turns
his head and walks away. You should:
   (a) Not go to the dance, and spend the evening
   fretting.
   (b) Ask your best friend what's wrong with you.
   (c) Have your brother or cousin take you.
   (d) Get some of that good-tasting "red stuff".

ANSWER: (d) *Get some of that good-tasting "red
stuff". A quart of Gallo or Thunder-
bird, chug-a-lugged, should help you forget about that crummy dance completely.*

3. John wants to show the best possible manners to his new girl. After picking her up in front of her home, he opened the door and let her go in first, then he closed the door, walked around to the other side, and got in himself. This showed good manners.
  (a) True
  (b) False

ANSWER: (a) *True. Actually, this did show good manners. However, if everyone did this, bus service would be slowed down considerably.*

4. A newly-married teenage couple should let their parents visit:
  (a) Twice a week
  (b) Once a week
  (c) Every other week
  (d) Once a month

ANSWER: (a) *A newly-married teenage couple should let their parents visit at least twice a week. After all, it is the parents' house.*

THE NATIONAL
CITY-DWELLER'S TEST

1. How much rent would you expect to pay for a decent three-room apartment in a big city?
  (a) $100 a month
  (b) $200 a month
  (c) $300 a month

ANSWER: *(a) (b) & (c) are all correct. Not individually, but added together. Yes, $600 a month is what a decent apartment rents for in a big city . . . unless, of course, you want to spend even more for "extras" like windows and doors and a wall to divide your apartment from the one next to you.*

2. At Christmas, you should give money to:
  (a) The Superintendent
  (b) The Mailman
  (c) The Doorman
  (d) None of the above

ANSWER: *(d) You are not obliged to give money to people like those listed above at Christmas time. The fool who does merely wants to avoid (a) being evicted, (b) having his mail thrown down a sewer, and (c) suffering a broken nose from having the front door slammed in his face.*

3. If your neighbors are noisy late at night, you should:
   (a) Call your neighbors
   (b) Report them to the police
   (c) Turn up your TV set
   (d) Do nothing

ANSWER: (a) *You should call your neighbors. Some of the things you can call them are:* "#$%@¢*&!" — "&%$#¢@+%!" —*and* "%&*#¢@#".

4. You should complain to your landlord if the temperature in your apartment falls below:
   (a) 60 degrees
   (b) 50 degrees
   (c) 40 degrees

ANSWER: *You can complain to your landlord if the temperature falls below* (a) *60 degrees. You can also complain if it falls below* (b) *50 degrees. You can even complain if it falls below* (c) *40 degrees. It won't do you any good. Landlords don't care what the heck temperature you complain at. They never listen.*

THE NATIONAL
TELEVISION VIEWER'S TEST

1. Huntley and Brinkley are:
   (a) Newscasters
   (b) Comedians
   (c) Brothers

   ANSWER: *We thought we'd start off this test with a real easy one. Of course, the answer is* **(b)** *Comedians, since the networks have been trying to make the news funnier and funnier lately.*

2. The Ed Sullivan Show has been entertaining television viewers on Sunday evenings for 15 years now.
   (a) True
   (b) False

   ANSWER: **(b)** *False. Although the Ed Sullivan Show **has** been on for 15 years, and **is** televised on Sunday evenings, the "key word" in this trick question is "entertaining".*

3. 90% of all prime time TV shows are in:
   (a) Black & white
   (b) Color
   (c) Bad taste

   ANSWER: (b) *Color. (Editor's Note to the millions who wrote* (c): *We feel a joke is a joke —and a lawsuit is a lawsuit!)*

4. If you want real action, the show to watch is:
   (a) The Man From U.N.C.L.E.
   (b) Batman
   (c) Hullabaloo

   ANSWER: *This question cannot be answered with a simple* (a), (b) *or* (c). *It would depend on your definition of "action". For example, if you wanted to see violence and fistfights and knifings and screaming, you would, of course, pick* (c) *Hullabaloo.*

5. The most talented man on TV is:
   (a) Lawrence Welk
   (b) Durward Kirby
   (c) Allen Ludden
   (d) Bert Parks

   ANSWER: *False.*

TWO WRIGHTS MADE A WRONG DEPT.

Contrary to popular belief, the writers at MAD are not always well-versed in the subjects they write about. Take this article, f'rinstance. The writer frankly admits that he has absolutely no faith in Air Travel. Not only has he never been in a plane in his life, but he even refuses to send out letters via Air Mail. He is very nervous about this Air Age we live in. In fact, the only way he relaxes is through his hobby: raising Homing Pigeons. And that hasn't worked out too well for him. Maybe it's because he makes the Pigeons travel by train! Oh— by the way, if this introduction seems ridiculous to you, forgive us. The idea of running another Primer is even more ridiculous!

THE MAD
AIR TRAVEL
PRIMER

Illustrated by George Woodbridge
Written by Larry Siegel

Chapter 1.
THE TAKE-OFF

See the busy airport.
See the busy terminal building in the busy airport.
See the nice airplane leaving the busy terminal building.
This is a 9:00 A.M. flight.
The airplane is leaving exactly on time.
Along the ground.
For another spot on the busy airport.
Where it will wait in line to take off.
Wait, wait, wait.
You won't be in the air for an hour yet.
Aren't long, delayed take-offs fun?
They give you more time to get settled in your seat.
They give you more time to admire the airport scenery.
They give you more time to pray!

Chapter 2.
THE LANDING

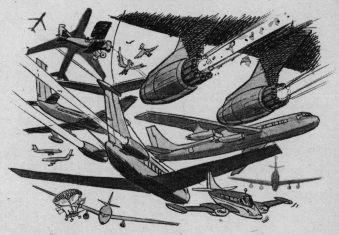

See the other nice airplane.
See it coming into the busy airport.
It is arriving in New York from Washington, D.C.
The whole trip took less than an hour.
See the nice airplane circling the busy New York Airport.
It will circle and circle.
For four hours.
Waiting for the plane circling underneath it to land.
Which is waiting for the plane circling underneath it to land.
Which is waiting for the plane circling underneath it to etc.
Etc., etc., etc.
Isn't air travel from Washington, D.C. to New York wonderful?
Sometimes, it's almost as quick as going by car!

Chapter 3.
THE HALF-FARE TEENAGERS

See the happy teenagers.
They are waiting to take advantage of an exciting offer.
The airline has promised them half-fare tickets.
If they are under 21 years of age.
There is just one catch to this offer.
They are on a "Stand-by" basis.
That means they must wait for cancellations.
That means they must wait until military people are taken care of.
That means they may have to wait quite a while.
By the time some of these teenagers finally get on a plane.
They will have to pay full-fare anyway.
Because they will be 22 years of age!

Chapter 4.
THE TYPICAL PASSENGER

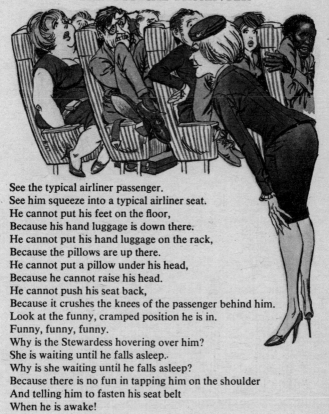

See the typical airliner passenger.
See him squeeze into a typical airliner seat.
He cannot put his feet on the floor,
Because his hand luggage is down there.
He cannot put his hand luggage on the rack,
Because the pillows are up there.
He cannot put a pillow under his head,
Because he cannot raise his head.
He cannot push his seat back,
Because it crushes the knees of the passenger behind him.
Look at the funny, cramped position he is in.
Funny, funny, funny.
Why is the Stewardess hovering over him?
She is waiting until he falls asleep.
Why is she waiting until he falls asleep?
Because there is no fun in tapping him on the shoulder
And telling him to fasten his seat belt
When he is awake!

Chapter 5.
THE STEWARDESS

See the nice Stewardess.
She is explaining how to use the life preservers.
She tells you where to find them.
She tells you how to put them on.
She tells you how to inflate them.
She tells you that they may save your life.
She asks if there are any questions.
Here is something to think about:
When was the last time you read of an airliner
Crash-landing in the sea and staying afloat
Long enough for passengers to get out
And use those life preservers?
Don't ask her that question!

Chapter 6.

THE FOOD

See the nice Stewardesses preparing the food.
Why do they dawdle so?
Because it is not yet time to serve the food.
Now they are putting the food on trays.
Why are they continuing to dawdle?
Because it is still not yet time to serve it.
Oh-oh! The plane is flying into a storm.
It is bouncing up and down.
Up and down.
Up (ugh!) and down (ugh!).
Now it is time to serve.
The Stewardesses always make sure
That the food is quickly distributed throughout the plane.
After it is served!

Chapter 7.
THE AIR SICKNESS BAG

See the nice passengers.
See them reach for their air sickness bags.
They are all violently ill.
Choke, gagg, urrrp!
Have they just eaten that nice airline food?
No.
Is the plane flying through a storm?
No.
Is it a bumpy flight?
No.
Then why are all the nice passengers sick?
Sick, sick, sick.
Oh, oh! Look up at the movie screen.
Now we know.
The airline is showing another Doris Day movie!

Chapter 8.

THE BAGGAGE CLAIM CHECK

See the happy passengers.
What a nice flight these passengers have had.
Now they are ready to claim their baggage.
Each passenger is holding his Baggage Claim Check.
But no one is looking at these Baggage Claim Checks.
They never do, at Baggage Return Sections.
See the happy man.
He is walking off with two nice leather suitcases.
Isn't that funny?
Before boarding the plane, that very same man
Checked in with only one piece of baggage:
A brown paper carton.
Isn't the Baggage Claim "Honor System" marvelous at airports?

Chapter 9.
THE DISTRAUGHT RELATIVE

See the anxious lady.
See how worried she is.
See how she paces up and down.
See how she wrings her hands.
Why is the lady so upset?
Her husband is on an airline flight.
And there is no telling what can happen.
Oh, oh! The telephone is ringing.
Ring, ring, ring.
The lady has just received the news that she has been dreading.
Her husband's plane has landed safely.
Another $200,000 Air Travel Insurance Policy shot to hell!

Chapter 10.
THE DISTRAUGHT NEIGHBORS

See the lovely house.
See the people who live in the lovely house.
See them cringe in fear and cover their heads.
See the windows shatter.
See the doors rattle.
See the dishes crash.
See the furniture splinter.
See the floor-boards quiver.
See the goldfish having heart attacks.
See the house leave its foundation.
Is the lovely house under an atomic attack?
No, the lovely house is under a Jet airliner
Taking off from the airport next door.
Isn't it fun living near an airport!

STILL

LATER ON IN THE HOSPITAL

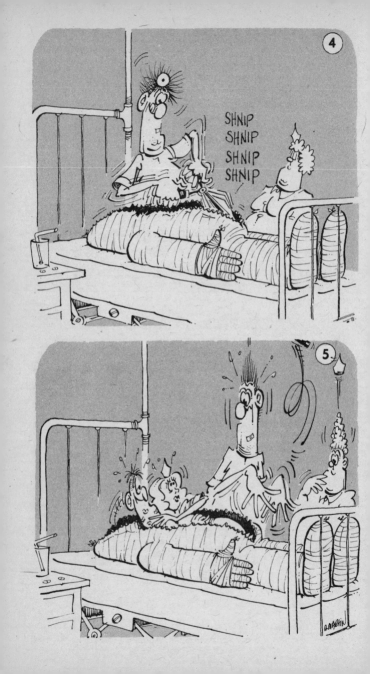

Everyone profits by using the U.S. Mails. Everyone, that is, except the U.S. Post Office Department, as their yearly deficit will attest. So we here at MAD have come up with a solution to this problem —mainly, *advertising!* Stamps are seen by millions of people daily, and the only messages that come through are things like "It's the 100th Anniversary of Groundhog Day" or "Celebrating the Bi-Centennial of the Founding of the U.S. Fertilizer Industry." These ridiculous "Commemoratives" bring nothing but the few pennies that the public pays for these stamps. What we suggest is that the Post Office Department get out of the red and into the long green by selling space for

POSTAGE STAMP ADVERTISING

ARTIST & WRITER: AL JAFFEE

STAMP ADS
IN MANY

"STAMP ADS" ARE ALREADY IN USE ON A SMALL SCALE

STAMP OUT POSTAGE STAMPS

Pitney-Bowes Postage Meter Corporation

Mr. Mel Haney
11 Veeblefetzer St.
Frammis, Ill.

Some "stamp advertising messages" already appear on mail. They are the messages printed by Postage Meters. But the profits from these all go to the Independent Meter-Maker.

Standard Post Office Dept. stamps could become highly desirable adver-

COULD BE USED
EXCITING WAYS

FUTURE "STAMP ADS" COULD ATTRACT BIG ADVERTISERS

HY POKONDRIAK'S
Pharmacy
666 Neurotic Rd.
Acheville, Ohio

Stomach Pills .. $7.99
Liver Pills $5.50
Heart Pills $9.00
Pill Pills $4.99

NOTICE: THIS BILL
IS THREE MONTHS
OVERDUE!

Special Offer!
Overdue Bill Pills--$7.99

Cowznofski
76 Ossefogva St.
Potrzebie, Ala.

ARM PITT
NOV.
31
1965
ALA.

With ads printed directly on stamps, the U.S. Government
would reap huge profits, and public would be treated to a
respite from those idiotic, meaningless commemoratives.

tising spaces for certain companies because of their
clever "message tie-in" value:

Advertisers could split the costs by participating in sheets of stamps the way sponsors do with "Special TV Shows." This would be especially effective when the products relate well to each other.

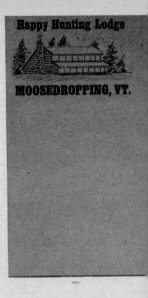

Other stamps, sold on rolls, could be used one at a time . . . or all at once to create amusing "teaser" effect that their road-sign counterparts produce:

| McGREGOR SPORTSWEAR | REMINGTON FIREARMS | HARTFORD ACCIDENT INSURANCE COMPANY | WINCHESTER AMMUNITION |

Myron Bloodthirsty,
27 Blastum Place,
Catskill, Ga. 67890

| BUT AT NIGHT | REFLECTING BRIGHT | THEY SAFELY GUIDE THE WAY! | Burma Shave |
| UNITED STATES POSTAGE | UNITED STATES POSTAGE | UNITED STATES POSTAGE | UNITED STATES POSTAGE |

For some advertisers, the "TV Story-Board" technique could be particularly appealing. Here's an example of an effective "TV Story-Board" stamp strip:

Everyone would collect odd-shaped stamps. A double-purpose could be served by producing them, since it is an ideal way to promote company trade-marks:

The largest volume of mail sent out by business organizations contains bad news for the public . . . mainly bills. To offset the bad feeling created by this necessary evil, bill-senders could use special stamps like these, that feature fun and entertainment, and make the recipient forget his troubles:

THE CONTINUITY SERIAL-STORY STAMP

Customers would look forward to each month's installment, and might even make unwanted purchases just to be sure of having a bill mailed to them.

THE ONE-PANEL GAG CARTOON STAMP

Popular magazine cartoonists would submit fresh gags for each month's new issue of these hilarious stamps.

THE SYNDICATED CARTOON STAMP

Famous Comic Characters could be used on stamps to get laughs. Value of such Public Relations to Bill-Mailers would be so great, they'd willingly use costly denominations for ordinary 5¢ letters.

On the local level, Postmasters would be authorized to accept small orders for special printings of stamps containing personal messages. For example:

ANNOUNCEMENTS

Stamps like these could be used as extra reminders of gifts due, etc. Excellent for notices of Engagements, Marriages, Births, Deaths, Divorces, Re-Marriages, etc.

ELECTIONEERING

Politicians couldn't resist this publicity gimmick, and P.O. Dept. would make money instead of losing it on all these free-loaders who can now mail their letters free.

FUN AND GAMES

Huge teenage market could be created with personal "Do-it-yourself" gag-type stamps. Besides profit for P.O. Dept., kids would also be forced to learn to write.

SALES GIMMICKS

Small "Mail-Order" outfits would find the personalized stamp a real boon with its easily-clipped-out coupon. (Note: Coupon is glueless on back for easy removal.)

PARTY POOPERS DEPT.

Have you noticed how more and more actors, writers, singers and others who deal with the public on one level are coming on at another level . . . mainly politics? What makes these people think that just because we enjoy their professional talents we're gonna enjoy their political philosophies, too? And what about other people in other professions? Suppose they followed this trend? Things could get pretty ridiculous! You'll see what we mean as MAD takes a look at . . .

THE DANGERS INHERENT IN
THIS TREND TOWARD...

MIXING

PERSONAL
POLITICS

WITH CAREERS

ARTIST: GEORGE WOODBRIDGE   WRITER: FRANK JACOBS

The **ULTRA-LIBERAL DEMOCRAT**
Restaurant
Owner...

What's this? Only half a steak?

Certainly! I suppose you're also against **Foreign Aid**! We sent the **other** half to **Afghanistan** to show them Americans want to share with needy people **everywhere**!

I—er—don't mean to sound ungrateful, but I don't **care** for Eggplant!

Haven't you heard of **Civil Rights?!** Eggplant is a **Minority Vegetable**! You'll **eat** it—and **like it**!

The JOHN BIRCH SOCIETY

Exterminator...

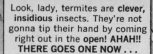

Look, lady, termites are **clever**, **insidious** insects. They're not gonna tip their hand by coming right out in the **open**! AHAH!! **THERE GOES ONE NOW . . .**

But that's just a house fly!

KRUNCH

It only **looks** like a housefly! It's **really** a termite in **disguise**! They'll go to **any** lengths to carry out their rotten, evil conspiracy to destroy your house!

But—but you're **wrecking** my **Living Room**!

The ULTRA-CONSERVATIVE

Used Car
Salesman...

Then how about this **1911 Stanley Steamer?** It was owned by a little old lady who used it only **once** . . . on Election Day in 1912, when she drove to the polls to vote for William Howard Taft, that great Repub—

Er—don't you have something more **modern?**

Surely you don't want an **assembly line model** built by men who belong to **Labor Unions!?** You look like a man who appreciates traditional American **craftsmanship!**

Oh, I do! I was thinking about—er— something like a **1928 Plymouth?**

The **COMMUNIST** Doctor...

The **SOCIALIST** Laundryman...

The **ANARCHIST** Pro-Football

Quarterback...

If you think this world out here is in a pretty sorry state, take a look at the troubles besetting those residents of that world-within-a-world as we present:

ANOTHER
MAD
Peek
Through The
MICRO-
SCOPE

ARTIST: PAUL COKER, JR.   WRITER: PHIL HAHN

What's wrong with Max? He's not very *communicable* this evening!

It's a clear case of *Germicide!*

I'm collecting for Polio Research! We're trying
to find a way to make it *incurable* again!

Name your *miracle drug!*

Ugly looking brute, isn't he?

The
President
just
appointed
him as
the new
*Chief
Of
Staph!*

He refuses to go to the Halloween Party!
He's afraid the *Hemoglobins*'ll get him!

That's funny! You don't look Germish!

He may *look* harmless, but he's deteriorated many a brain in his time!

A MAD LOOK AT TRADE-MARKS

WRITTEN AND DESIGNED BY: MAX BRANDEL

ENOVI D
PILL
ORAL CONTRACEPTIVE

Johnson WAX

Ot s
ELEVATOR COMPANY

ScotTissue

PAN   M

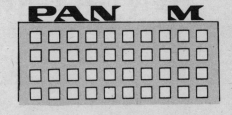

Firestone

PLAYBOY

CONTAC

against sniffles, sneezes, and stuffy nose.

AV II S
RENT-A-CAR

Xeroxxxxxxxxxxxxxxxxxxxxxxxxxxxxx

7 ^rup

ROBERT HALL

Young & Rubicam
advertising

XXXXXXXXXXXXXXXXXXXXXXXXXXXXXX

RADIO CITY

THE LIGHTER SIDE OF...

HIGH SCHOOL

WRITER & ARTIST: DAVID BERG

Sororities are absolutely **stupid!** They're nothing but **snobbish in-groups!** Right now, they're looking for prospective members in a **stupid ritual** called **"Rushing"!** It's a **terribly cruel blow** to the girls they **don't accept!**

Then there's **another stupid ritual** called **"Pledging"!** That's when they **mark up your face** and make you wear **ridiculous clothes** and force you to walk around the campus and in town, doing **idiotic things!**

CENTRAL HIGH

Then there's **"Hell Night"**, another **stupid ritual** where they make you suffer **further indignities** before they admit you as a full-fledged **"Sister"!** **No wonder** so many High Schools have **outlawed** Sororities!

RING

Hey, **Lion-in-a-Cage!** What's with **you?** All evening long, you've been pacing up and down, up and down . . .

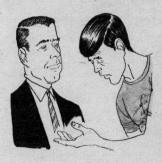

It's that **exam** I'm having tomorrow! I'm really **worried** about it!

If you spent as much time **studying** for it as you spend **worrying** about it, you'd be much better off!

Studying for it?! How can I **study** for it when I'm **so upset?!**

I was just thinking: Remember how, when the kids were **young** and they'd have a party down in the playroom, they'd get so noisy we'd have to yell, "**HEY, YOU, DOWN THERE! CUT OUT THAT NOISE!**"?

But now that they're **older** and going to **High School**, their parties are so **nice** and quiet . . .

NICE AND QUIET?!?

HEY, YOU, DOWN THERE! LET'S HEAR A LITTLE **NOISE**!!

Beverly, darling! I've **met** him! **Mr. Right!** It was one of those magical things that happens only once in a lifetime, and it took place right in my own **Homeroom!** I'll never forget it if I **live** forever . . . even **longer!!**

We were passing out IBM cards and our **hands** touched. It was like **electricity.** We both knew instantly. Now, we're going steady, and it's all figured out. The day he graduates from **college**, we'll be married!

I know! I know! You told me all about this **last week!**

Last week?! Oh, that was Bob Green! I'm talking about **Martin Drabb!** That's this week!

Like **what**, f'rinstance?

Like she has a **cute brother**—and he's going to **Med School!**

When I get my diploma, I'll finally be able to go to **college** and fulfill my **parents'**—and also **MY greatest dream**—I'll meet a **fella!!**

When they hand me my diploma, I can just hear my kid brother saying, "Now that she's going off to **college**, I'll finally have the **bathroom** all to myself!"

For three years, I've worked like a **son-of-a-gun** to graduate! Now, in just a very short time, they're going to hand me the thing I've **slaved** for . . . the **keys to the car** my folks promised me!

David Berg

A MAD LOOK AT BATMAN

ARTIST & WRITER: SERGIO ARAGONES

—SLURG!! SLURG!!

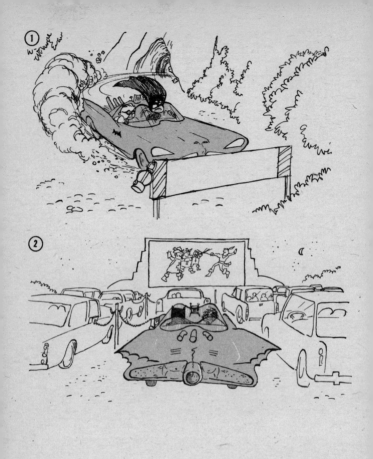

11